FLUTE Prep Test

This book belongs to:

....

Date of Prep Test:

....

Examiner's signature:

....

The Associated Board of the Royal Schools of Music

Sunset in Paris

Sarah Watts

Flute Prep Test

Piano Accompaniments

Showtime

Sarah Watts

AB 3418

FLUTE PREP TEST

Dear flute player

Congratulations! You have reached a stage when you can play to an examiner and achieve your first certificate. The skills you will use include a sense of pitch and rhythm, accuracy and making a pleasant and even sound or 'tone'. You will be with the examiner for about 10 minutes, during which time you will play the tunes, pieces and answer the listening games. You may have your own accompanist for the pieces or the examiner can accompany you. The examiner's comments and suggestions will be written on the certificate given to you at the end of the test. You might like to have it framed, so that it will always be a reminder of this special occasion.

I hope you enjoy the tunes, pieces and listening games in this book, as well as the illustrations and Fun Page. This is the first step on what will be an exciting and lifelong musical journey.

Now on to the music!

Clara Taylor

Clara Taylor
Chief Examiner

AB 3418

1 Tunes

The examiner will want to hear you play all three of these tunes. You will have to play them from memory, so once you have learnt them remember to keep your book closed when you are practising!

a) Make it Smooth

Play this piece quietly with a clear and even sound. Remember to tongue carefully and hold the long notes for their full value.

b) Make it Snappy

This is a jumpy piece! The notes with dots underneath should be tongued and played short and light (this is called *staccato*).

c) Make it Long

In this slow piece, play the long notes with an even sound. Are you making the fullest sound you can?

2 Set Piece

Your set piece can be any one of the five pieces printed on pages 6, 7, 8 and 9 – 'Hot Dog Hoedown', 'Snail Trails', 'Pigeon Parade', 'Showtime' or 'Sunset in Paris'. Alternatively, you may choose any piece from *Party Time!* for Flute (published by ABRSM Publishing). If you choose 'Showtime', 'Sunset in Paris' or a piece from *Party Time!*, either your accompanist or the examiner will play it with you. Your teacher will help you to choose the right piece.

Hot Dog Hoedown

Sarah Watts

Snail Trails

Sarah Watts

Smoothly ♩ = c.128

Pigeon Parade

Sarah Watts

Bright and happy ♩ = c.130

Showtime

Sarah Watts

Sunset in Paris

Sarah Watts

3 Own Choice Piece

We would like you to play this with either your accompanist or the examiner, so you need to choose a piece with a piano accompaniment. As we want you to play something you really enjoy, we have left the choice up to you. If you like, you can play one of the accompanied set pieces from this book, as long as it is different from you first piece! Whichever piece you choose, remember to bring the piano part for whoever is accompanying you.

4 Listening Games

In these games the examiner will be playing pieces of music like the examples printed below.

Game A: Clapping the beat

In this first game, the examiner will play a short piece in 2 or 3 time. You should join in as soon as possible by clapping or tapping the beat.

All music has a beat, so you can practise this game at home with your friends whenever you are listening to music on the radio or a recording.

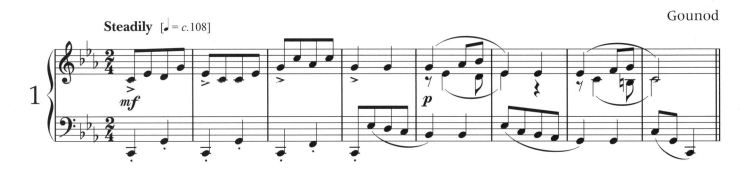

Game B: Echoes

In this game, the examiner will clap two simple two-bar rhythms in 2 or 3 time. After each one, you should clap the rhythm back to the examiner in time and as an echo. The examiner will count in two bars before the first rhythm.

Practise this game at home with a friend or parent. Did you clap *exactly* the same rhythm? Did you clap it back in rhythm or was there a pause?

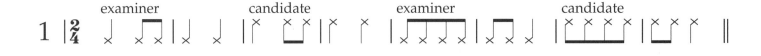

Game C: Finding the notes

Now the examiner will play a group of three notes to you, two times through. The game is to sing these notes back to the examiner after the second playing. They will be played in 'free time', so you don't need to worry about the rhythm. If you don't want to sing, you can play the notes on your flute, in which case the examiner will play a group using only G, A and B – you have to find all three notes, including the starting note! Here are some examples:

Game D: What can you hear?

In this last game, listen as the examiner plays another short piece of music. The examiner will want to know whether the piece was played loudly or quietly (the 'dynamic' of the piece), or whether it was fast or slow (the 'tempo' of the piece). The examiner will choose one of these and tell you which one to listen out for before he or she plays.

Practise this game at home with your friends whenever you are playing or listening to a piece of music.

i) Is this piece loud or quiet?

ii) Is this piece fast or slow?

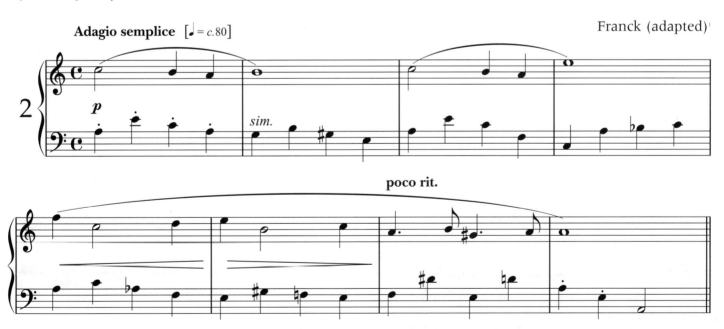

Fun Page

Music is written down on five lines known as a 'stave'. A few empty staves are printed below: you can use these to practise drawing notes, rests, clefs and time signatures (if you don't understand any of these words, ask your teacher or look in *First Steps in Music Theory*, published by ABRSM Publishing). Or you can write down some tunes of your own.

Word Search

This word search contains 12 musical words, listed below. How many can you find? Do you know what they all mean?

Words to find:
octave
note
rhythm
legato
tone
staccato
flute
tonguing
dynamic
keys
pitch
tempo

N	A	F	B	D	J	E	C	N	Z
T	O	N	G	U	I	N	G	E	F
A	C	T	C	I	E	O	R	T	S
P	T	G	E	V	C	T	X	U	T
I	A	B	F	K	C	P	T	L	A
T	V	Q	M	E	A	G	E	F	C
C	E	P	D	Y	N	A	M	I	C
H	G	A	U	S	T	F	P	A	A
M	H	T	Y	H	R	W	O	L	T
F	L	J	A	L	E	G	A	T	O

We hope you enjoyed doing the Prep Test and look forward to seeing you at Grade 1!

05.08   Printed in England by Halstan & Co. Ltd, Amersham, Bucks